NEW WORLD NEIGHBORS

NEW WORLD NEIGHBORS

Up to the north, extending from the Great Lakes and the Forty-ninth parallel to the Arctic seas, is a country much like the United States, yet different. It is an old country but also young and new. More than three hundred years ago it was settled by the French, and today there are over three million descendants of these early settlers, mostly in Quebec. They still speak French as their mother tongue and preserve in rural Quebec the ways of the France of olden times.

Most Canadians, however, are of English-speaking origin, descendants of people who came to Canada from the British Isles during the last two hundred years. They made their first homes in the east, but their descendants spread westward through prairie and mountain to the far Pacific. They have cleared the forests, dug mines, built cities, highways, and railroads, and have brought civilization to the most remote places. Canadians live as do people of the United States, some in the cabin of the pioneer, others in the comfortable town and country houses of older and more prosperous communities.

Canada is a free, democratic country, united under the British Crown with the other nations of the British Empire for the preservation of just such liberty as Americans also know and defend. This common love of liberty should make us friends.

This book is mainly about British Columbia, the most westerly Canadian province. We who live here think it a beautiful country. You can easily reach us by motor car, ship, and train. You will be welcome anywhere in Canada.

—H. B. KING
Chief Inspector of Schools
British Columbia

UP
CANADA WAY

By HELEN DICKSON

Illustrated by

FLORA NASH DeMUTH

D. C. HEATH AND COMPANY

BOSTON · NEW YORK · CHICAGO · ATLANTA
SAN FRANCISCO · DALLAS · LONDON

BRITISH
COLUMBIA

British Columbia is a country of mountains and forests, with a belt of sandy soil and sage-brush down the center. The long sea coast is indented with fjords like those of Norway, and protected from the gales of the Pacific by many islands. The climate is temperate, and made pleasant and bracing by sea breezes. In many ways, British Columbia is much like the states of Washington, Idaho, and Montana.

In the interior, mining and smelting, lumbering, fruit growing, and cattle ranching are the principal occupations. There are many busy towns in the interior, but no large cities.

On the coast, lumbering, fishing, and canning are the basic industries, and there are factories for many products. Shipping and ship-building play an important part in the industrial life of the people.

Vancouver and Victoria are cities of great scenic beauty, with fine harbors, airports, parks, and beaches. The people dress as we do and live in similar houses and bungalows of frame, stucco, and brick. They have excellent schools, art schools, tech-

4

nical schools, and a university. The arts receive a great deal of attention, especially music and drama.

In many cities and towns in Canada musical festivals are held every spring and summer. Three or four well-known musicians and elocutionists come from England to act as judges and choose the winners. They give marks and award certificates, tell each contestant the faults and merits of his performance, and often give a short lesson. There are classes for grown-ups and children, for choirs, orchestras, vocal and instrumental solos, recitations, and folk dances. In the last twenty years, these music festivals have become increasingly popular and have served to raise the standards of the whole province in music appreciation and performance.

Once a year school children of Vancouver meet school children of the State of Washington at the Peace Arch at Blaine, on the international boundary, to take part in a ceremony celebrating over a hundred years of peace between the United States and Canada.

MACS ARE ROLLING

The roar of a passing truck awakened Lester. That was the worst of a bed on the veranda. You could not sleep late, even on Saturday morning. A second truck went by, and Lester realized what it meant. He sprang out of bed. "Macs are rolling," he thought, and dashed into the house to dress.

McIntosh Reds, the big juicy apples that have made the Okanagan Valley famous, were ripe and ready for shipment. Lester's father had promised to take the family to a show on Saturday evening, if the Macs in the home orchard were picked by four o'clock. They must be ready to haul to the packing house by then.

"Where's everybody?" Lester asked his mother a few minutes later, in the sunny kitchen. Dressed in overalls, she was tying a yellow kerchief over her brown curls, to keep them from catching in apple tree branches.

"Nancy has gone to the packing house, Jill is picking, and Dad has started hauling Major Paton's Macs to the packing house. He had the truck serviced and bought a drum of gas. It took our last cent, so I hope Major Paton will pay him today. Are you ready to work?"

"I'll be out in a few minutes." Lester served himself a bowlful of porridge from the double boiler at the back of the stove.

"I'm going out to pick now," his mother said. "You'll find bacon and toast in the warming oven. Be sure to put the porridge pot to soak."

When he had eaten his breakfast, Lester wriggled his head and arms into the straps of a picking-bag and went out to the orchard. Heads in red and blue kerchiefs looked like bright birds among the dark green leaves of the apple trees. The clatter of tongues made it sound as if a flock of parrots were picking the apples. Grace and Tom Wilson, whose family lived on the next ranch, were helping.

The boughs bent till many of them touched the ground, under their load of deep crimson apples. Lester picked those he could reach from the ground; then he set up a ladder. He was up the ladder among the branches before he remembered that he had not put the porridge pot to soak.

"Jiminy," he muttered. "I can't go back now."

Lester was a quick picker and knew just the twist that brings an apple off without breaking the fruit spur. He had long hands for a boy of eleven and could pick with both at once, holding three apples in each hand. He was careful, too, and emptied his bag into the orchard box so gently that the apples were not bruised.

Piles of orchard boxes were lying under each tree. Lester wondered how many Jill had filled. He didn't want his sister to beat him in the day's picking, even though she was two years older.

"How many boxes have you picked, Jill?" he called out.

"Six."

"I'll be ahead of you by noon."

Jill laughed. "You'll have to snap into it, Les. I have a good start."

Lester worked fast. He was thinking that when Dad had finished hauling Major Paton's Macs, he would take the boxes from the home ranch. That would give Lester a chance for a ride to the packing house, if his job were finished.

The sky seen through the leaves was a deep, wonderful blue. The sun filled the orchard with drowsy warmth, and bees were humming. The pickers laughed and talked, sang and whistled, while truckload after truckload from other orchards roared past on the dusty road.

Lester's mother and Jill were picking the next tree, and beyond that Grace and Tom Wilson were working. Lester did a little rough figuring. There were eight trees of Macs that would yield an average of thirty boxes each. That made two hundred and forty boxes to be picked by five pickers.

"That's easy," he thought. "We'll be finished by two o'clock."

9

He worked faster yet, because he wanted to catch up to Jill and beat her. Besides, Dad gave him five cents for every box he picked, and he was saving to buy a camera. He wished Dad had more trees of Macs, because they were easy to pick and brought a good price. Most of the trees in the orchard were later apples and not so popular. That was one reason why Dad had to haul apples for other groves.

"Hiya, Jill," Lester called out. "How many boxes have you picked now?"

"Eighteen."

"I'm catching up with you. You were six ahead of me, but now you are only four ahead."

"You won't be even by noon, just the same."

At his sister's challenge Lester put on a spurt.
He went quickly down the ladder with a full bag,
opened the flap at the bottom and let the apples roll
into an empty box. They made so much noise that
he glanced around uneasily. His mother looked
down from the top of a ladder.

"Lester!" she cautioned. "Please be more careful
how you empty your bag. Macs bruise so easily.
Sometimes a bruise won't show for weeks and then
a brown spot will appear under the skin."

"I'll be careful, Mother," Lester promised, as
he hurried up the ladder again. He came to a bough

on which the apples were extra large, so that he was able to fill his bag quickly.

"I must have thinned this tree," he thought.

In the early summer Jill and he had helped to pick off the young apples. They left only one on a fruit spur, or none, spacing the small, green apples four inches apart. This was to allow the remaining apples to grow large and well rounded. Now, he was reaping the benefit of that work.

"Oh, boy," he thought, "I'll soon catch up with Jill."

Tom Wilson came with the tallest ladder to pick the high top branches that could not be reached by the ordinary ladders. It was heavy, and needed a strong man to handle it.

"I could pick the tops by climbing," Lester thought, "but it would be slow work."

At half past eleven Mother went to the house to heat some soup. At noon she rang a gong. The welcome sound brought the pickers hurrying down from their ladders. Just then a truck drove up to the gate and the driver called out, "Is Tom Wilson there?"

"I'm here," Tom replied.

"Your father sent you a message. He needs you to drive the truck this afternoon."

"All right," Tom agreed, taking off his picking-bag. "I'll go right home." He started toward the gate.

Lester ran after him. "Tom, how can we pick the tops if you go? I can't carry that ladder."

"Sorry," Tom said. "You'll have to manage some way. If Dad needs me, I have to go."

Lester saw the prospect of the trip to town and a show becoming suddenly dim. He turned to meet Jill and Grace Wilson.

"I don't see how we can do it," he said. "How many boxes have you picked, Jill?"

"Twenty-eight."

"Now that Tom's gone, we'll have a hard job to pick the Macs by four o'clock."

"We'll have a quick lunch and go back," Jill said.

Grace had brought her own sandwiches, but Mother insisted that she should have a bowl of

13

vegetable soup as well. Mother looked worried when she heard that Tom had gone home.

"Who will pick the tops?" she asked.

"I'll have to climb and bend the tops over so that one of you can pick them," Lester said. "I won't be able to race you, Jill, but that doesn't matter so much as having the picking done by four o'clock."

As soon as they had eaten their lunch, they hurried back to the orchard. Lester tried to use the topping ladder, but it was too heavy, even when his mother helped him.

"I'll have to climb," he decided.

"Do be careful," his mother begged. "I'm so afraid you will fall."

But Lester was not afraid, as he stepped lightly from one strong limb to another. He bent the long top branches over, and Jill, on a ladder, could reach to pick off the apples. Mother and Grace Wilson went on with the lower branches.

It was slow work, but Lester and Jill kept on until tree after tree was left with only dark green leaves. Finally there was just one tree top left to pick.

"Oh, hurry!" Mother called up to them. "It's half past three."

"Dad isn't here yet," Lester answered, "and it will take him a while to load the picked boxes. Oh! There he comes now."

Dad drove along between the rows of trees. He stopped at each pile of boxes and loaded them on the truck, while the pickers worked furiously to finish. When the last box was in, Jill and Lester hopped into the cab of the truck beside their father.

"We did it!" Jill cried happily and then, after a moment, "Dad, did Major Paton pay you?"

"Yes, I'm glad to say he did," Dad replied. "If we hurry, we can still go to the show."

Dad drove at fifty miles an hour along the straight stretch on the way to the packing house, for the apples must be started "rolling." That is what they say in the Okanagan Valley when the fruit cars move on the railroad.

While Dad was unloading the forty-pound boxes, Jill and Lester stood at the door watching the four big graders at work. Their wide belts moved slowly along, with lines of marching apples which rolled into bins, each apple separated with others its own size.

The packers were too busy to look up or notice them, and the graders made so much noise it was no use to speak. The packers' hands moved so fast they were a blur, as they wrapped each apple in paper with one skilful twist and packed it in order in the box. Rustlers were hurrying about with wheeled carriers, taking packed boxes to the nailers. Then the nailers put the lids on and brought fresh orchard boxes to the graders.

The only person who noticed Jill and Lester was their older sister Nancy, who spared time for a

smile and a quick wave. She was sorting apples from orchard boxes to the belt of the grader and culling those with blemishes.

As soon as Dad had unloaded they drove home. Jill went in to help Mother, and Lester ran to the wood pile. Mother would need plenty of kindling and firewood to cook a good dinner for hungry workers. When he came into the kitchen with an armful of wood, his mother greeted him with a complaint.

"Lester, you didn't soak the porridge pot and now I can't start the porridge for the morning."

"Jiminy!" Lester wailed. "I forgot. I meant to do it at noon. I'll scrub it out now, Mother."

He started work with hot water, scouring powder, and a brush. In a moment, he let out another wail. "I forgot my bantams, too. They haven't been fed yet. I guess I'll have to get along without dinner if I want to go to the show."

Jill came to his rescue. "I'll feed your bantams, Les. And if the porridge pot is not finished when I come in, I'll take a turn to let you wash and change."

Lester reflected that sisters were not so bad after all, as he put more energy into his scrubbing. How that oatmeal did stick! "It would make grand glue," he muttered.

Dinner was on the table, and still Lester had not won the battle with the porridge pot.

"Sorry, Mother. I'm afraid I won't have time to eat dinner." He looked very sad and hungry.

"Come along, Les," Jill laughed. "I'll finish that old double boiler for you after dinner."

Lester came gratefully. Corn on the cob, sausages with potatoes and squash, tomatoes ripe from the vine, home-canned peaches and bran muffins made him feel like a new boy. Now he was ready for the evening's fun.

"Go and dress, Les," Jill said as she cleared the table, "and I'll finish the porridge pot."

Everyone rushed around, doing his own job as fast as possible. By the time Dad drove the truck up to the door, the dishes were washed and put away in the glass cupboard, the porridge pot shone, and the family looked trim in town-going clothes. Mother sat in the cab with Dad, and Jill, Lester, and Nancy had a rug and cushions in the back of the truck.

Town was gay and lively with cars parked all along the main street, while growers, pickers, and packers enjoyed their Saturday evening. After the show, everyone flocked to the ice cream parlor, and since they all knew one another, it was like a large party.

"I brought some apples," Mother said as they climbed into the truck to drive home. "Anybody want one?"

There was a reaching out of eager hands for the first Macs of the season, as they jolted happily over the washboard road. Under a yellow moon in the sage-brush scented air, they munched with quiet satisfaction the crimson apples that spurted delicious juice at every bite.

Life is merry, indeed, in the Okanagan Valley when Macs are rolling.

WHEN THE SOCKEYE RUN

Uncle Jeff's voice rang through the house. "I tell you I won't have you going around with young Beekman," he declared. "You know that there's been trouble between his dad and me for years. I don't want any of the boys coming here."

The color flamed in Andy's face, but he only said quietly, "Tod Beekman has been my friend since long before I came to work for you, Uncle Jeff. You can't expect me to give up my best friend, just because you had a quarrel with his dad. That's asking more than is fair."

Andy's young brother Joe said nothing, but he

was worried, because he liked Tod Beekman's twelve-year-old brother Pete.

"It's no use arguing," Uncle Jeff replied. "It's my house and my boat and I have a right to say who'll come in them."

He stumped out of the house and down the landing which the outgoing tide had left lying at a slant. His quick burst of temper had stolen some of his control, so that he walked carelessly and slipped on a strand of seaweed. He fell with a fearful thud and gave a cry of pain.

Andy and Joe hurried out and helped him to his feet. Uncle Jeff held his right arm and moaned, "Broken . . . feels broken."

"We'd better get you to the Mission Hospital," Andy said. Andy was the practical member of the family. Now he helped his uncle to the fishing boat at the end of the long landing-stage. Uncle Jeff's home was on the coast of British Columbia, a few miles from one of the Mission hospitals.

Uncle Jeff was not the man to bear pain patiently. He sat moaning in the cabin while Andy started the engine and steered for the hospital. There the doctor took an X-ray. The small bone of the arm was cracked, and there were severe bruises. With his arm in a sling, Uncle Jeff was permitted to go home.

"You boys will have to take the *Nellie M* out tonight," he growled. "It's just my luck to be laid up when the sockeye are running. The weather doesn't look too good, either," he added, squinting at the clouds.

About the first of July the legal season for sockeye opens. Andy and Joe knew that at this season the sockeye salmon, the best species for canning, come in from the Pacific in schools of many thousands. The sockeye that have reached mature years, that is, four or five, seek the rivers in which they were spawned.

During the sockeye run there is a closed season of forty-eight hours once a week. This is to allow some salmon to escape and go up the rivers to spawn. If it were not for this closed season the sockeye would soon vanish from the sea.

When the sun set and the sea turned to blue-black ink, Andy and Joe put on sweaters and went to the *Nellie M,* their uncle's boat. Joe was very much excited, because he was seldom allowed to go in the boat at night. It was a still night, very dark and brooding, with a hint of thunder in the air. The little boat chug-chugged steadily through the smooth, dark water to the fishing ground.

While Joe took a nap in the cabin bunk, Andy shut off the engine and let out the gill-net. There was a lantern at the end of the line of cedar floats that held up the net. Lead sinkers held the bottom edge down, and the net was like a wall of diamond-shaped holes for the salmon to poke their heads in.

Fish cannot swim backward, so the salmon are caught by the gills.

After a few hours, Andy drew in the net by starting the engine and catching the net to a drum in the after part of the boat. The drum rolled up the net while Andy and Joe took out the fish—twenty sockeyes and four "humpies." The sockeye salmon weighed seven or eight pounds apiece and were worth much more than the humpies.

"You've had some sleep, Joe," Andy said when he had let the net out for a second "drift" and shut off the engine. "Watch this drift while I get a little. I'm afraid of the wind getting up while I'm asleep." He turned into the bunk.

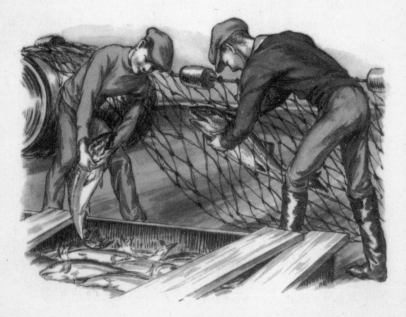

Joe watched anxiously as the lantern at the end of the line of floats tossed and dipped. Far off through the murky night, he could see the riding lights of the Beekmans' boat. He wondered how Tod and Pete felt about the rising wind.

A big wave sent spray over the gunwale. Joe wondered if he ought to awaken Andy. Soon he noticed that the lights of the Beekmans' boat were moving toward the harbor.

"I guess we'd be wise to follow," he decided. "Say, Andy," he shook his brother's shoulder, "wake up. The wind's coming up strong."

Andy opened his eyes and blinked at the light, then rolled out of the bunk and looked at the weather. "Uh-huh," he grunted.

They ran the net in and took out the catch, while the spray came over the bow and the *Nellie M* plunged and rolled. Then Andy took the wheel.

The lights of the other boat moved ahead. After a time Andy found himself gaining on it, and presently he was abeam. A voice hailed him.

As he steered closer, Tod's older brother, Jack, shouted to him, "Engine's stopped! Can you give us a tow?"

Andy eased the *Nellie M* closer yet and a little ahead, while Joe threw a line to Tod who caught and made it fast.

"All right," Tod shouted, "you can go ahead."

It was a difficult job of towing. The *Nellie M* was a small boat, with only two feet of freeboard when she rode light. Suddenly the other boat's engine started, and the rope slackened.

"We're casting off," Tod shouted. "We've tinkered her up. Thanks for the tow."

"You're welcome!" Joe shouted back. The Beekmans' boat labored astern while the *Nellie M*, freed from the drag, bounced ahead.

Without warning, a wave struck the *Nellie M* a blow that nearly keeled her over. Andy felt a tightness in his throat.

"She won't stand many like that," he thought. The water was sloshing about his ankles. A minute later he saw a wall of water rising up and over the boat. The rush of water tore Andy from the wheel and dashed him against the wall of the pilot house as the *Nellie M* capsized.

Andy and Joe battled to the surface. The boat had righted herself, but she was full of water. Only the pilot house was clear, and Andy caught Joe and dragged him to it. There they clung, while slowly the dawn light showed the plight of the *Nellie M*— half sunk and the dinghy lost. Cold gray-green water washed over her as the chilled boys clung desperately to the pilot house.

Time passed like a bad dream from which they could not awake. Andy tried to shout, but salt water filled his mouth and his voice was lost in the roar of waves. Gradually, the dawn brightened and to the boys' relief the wind dropped, so that they were not flung about so cruelly.

"Are you all right, Joe?" Andy asked, but Joe

could not speak. Andy uncramped one hand and put it round Joe.

As they rose on the crest of a wave, Andy caught a glimpse of a fishing boat in the offing. Once more he tried to shout. After another long wait, he heard the chugging of her engine, growing louder every minute. The fishing boat nosed in beside the half-sunk *Nellie M*. Andy heard a welcome voice. Then a long arm reached over and grabbed Andy's sweater. It was Tod Beekman.

More hands reached down, and soon the two boys were in the Beekmans' boat. The Beekmans carried them to the cabin, stripped them of their wet clothes, and wrapped them in blankets. They gave them hot cocoa to drink.

"Shall we go back for the *Nellie M?*" Tod asked. "Can we tow her in?"

"She'll drag like a whale," Jack Beekman said, "and our engine isn't behaving any too well."

"We can pump her out and she'll tow all right," Tod said hopefully.

"You can try if you like." Jack was grateful for the help he had received from the *Nellie M* during the night.

The wind had dropped, but there was still a heavy swell, and the *Nellie M* fell out of sight in the trough. Andy rolled out of the Beekmans' bunk.

He was tough and springy, like a salmon, and it took more than a dose of "salt chuck" to exhaust him.

"Where are my clothes?" he asked. "I'll give a hand." He dragged on his damp trousers and an old sweater Tod kept in the bunk, and was ready to help save his uncle's boat. Tod swung the wheel over and turned back to look for the water-filled *Nellie M*. When they came near her, Andy ran the dinghy out, and he and Jack Beekman jumped in and rowed to the *Nellie M*.

They stepped into the half-sunk boat and fastened the dinghy's painter to a cleat. Standing knee deep in water they worked, Andy with the hand pump, Jack Beekman bailing with a bucket. Finally the *Nellie M* regained enough buoyancy to tow with a fair amount of ease. Then they signaled to Tod to throw them a line.

Tod had been going around the *Nellie M* in circles, slowly, waiting for the word. Now he came close, and Pete Beekman heaved the bight of a rope to Andy's hand.

"All set!" Andy shouted as soon as he had made the rope fast. Tod set the engine full speed ahead, and the *Nellie M* followed. The two aboard continued their efforts to get all the water out. After a while Andy and Beekman traded jobs. Jack pumped and Andy bailed, until the boat was dry. By that time the sun was up, with promise of a bright day, and the morning haze was lifting from the sea.

Meanwhile, aboard the Beekmans' boat, Joe was reviving. He still felt a curious weariness and his fingers were blue at the tips, but strength was coming back to him rapidly. The youngest Beekman boy, Pete, put bacon and salmon to fry on the oil stove, and the odor made Joe hungry. Breakfast was the one thing he needed to put him on his feet.

Pete brought him a plate heaped with bright red salmon steaks and crisp slices of bacon. After he had

eaten that, he had a mug of coffee and a slice of bread and marmalade.

"Tastes fine," Joe said. "Thanks."

Pete went up to take the wheel and give Tod a chance to eat.

"I wonder what my dad will say when he sees you in our boat and hears how you gave us a tow," Tod said to Joe as he entered the cabin.

"Your dad?" Joe looked up in surprise. "I was just wondering the same thing about my uncle. There was some old fuss between them, and Uncle Jeff asked us not to go around with you."

"Is that so?" This time it was Tod who sounded amazed. "It's about time they forgot it."

Joe shrugged his shoulders and lay down in the bunk. His muscles were strained and sore from clinging to the boat. He examined his bruised and cut knuckles.

"Some storm," he muttered. "First time I ever heard of a fishing boat capsizing."

"My dad's boat capsized near Cape Caution once,

but that's a dangerous ground," said Tod. "You rest a while longer. I'm going back on deck."

Wallowing through oily seas, they crept into harbor. In the early sunlight they could see two figures on the landing. One man was stout, with a white sling. That would be Uncle Jeff. The other, tall and spare, the Beekman boys recognized as their father.

As they came nearer the boys could see the tall figure slap the stout one on the back and point.

"Looks as if they'd forgotten their quarrel," Tod said, grinning.

As the boat came alongside the landing, Dad Beekman caught the hawser Pete threw and warped the boat in.

"Had some trouble?" he asked drily, to conceal his relief. "We've been worried about you."

"I'll say we had trouble," Pete replied. "Engine trouble, and Andy towed us till we tinkered her up. Then a bull wave capsized the *Nellie M,* and we went in circles trying to pick them up until it was light enough to see."

Uncle Jeff was shading his eyes to look at his boat and wondering why he didn't see Joe.

"So you brought the *Nellie M* in, too," he said gruffly. "I'll pay you what's right for towing."

"Is it towing or salvage?" Dad Beekman asked quickly.

Tod came out of the pilot house. He knew that salvage would cost Andy's uncle much more than towing. "Either way, we're even, Dad. Let's call it square and forget your old quarrel. What was it all about, anyway?"

"Jiggered if I can remember," Uncle Jeff admitted. He held out his hand to Dad Beekman, who shook it with a sheepish grin.

In the cabin, Joe was hastily pulling on his half-dry clothes. He was afraid that if he appeared wrapped in a blanket he would be regarded as a kid, and never allowed out fishing again at night. As he climbed over the gunwale his uncle asked, "Had enough of gill-netting, Joe?"

"I liked it fine," Joe replied, jauntily, holding up one big salmon he had saved when the boat capsized.

SHE SHALL
HAVE MUSIC

A bell tinkled and the girl in front of Joan moved forward. Joan followed with her heart beating faster than usual. It was the first time she had been allowed to sing with the school choir at the Vancouver Music Festival. Her whole mind was bent on singing her part perfectly. It would be a great honor to win the choir contest and she wanted to do her best for her school. This year there were nearly forty school choirs taking part.

Behind a big desk the judge and his assistant sat with pencils and score sheets. They would record a note held a sixteenth too long, or cut a fraction too short, or sung a hair's breadth off the key. Not only that, the judge insisted that the full meaning of music and words must be expressed. The great man from England who presided over the annual music contest was just, kind, and helpful, but very critical.

Thirty boys and girls from Joan's school, all wearing their school colors on their shoulders, filed out on the stage. Mothers and friends in the auditorium smiled at them with encouragement, but the choir stood absolutely silent, waiting for the second bell.

Ping! The little bell tinkled again, and thirty pairs of eyes watched for the lift of the conductor's baton. Joan moistened her lips and opened her mouth. Soon she forgot to be afraid and sang as if she loved singing.

The Festival piece they were singing was a setting of Kipling's poem, "Where are you going to, all you big steamers?" Joan knew where the big steamers were going, for her father was chief engineer in an oil tanker. As long as she could remember, she had seen the big steamers come in and go out of the port of Vancouver in British Columbia.

Joan's choir was the last to sing. When they had finished they took their seats in the auditorium and waited with anxiety for the judge's report. The judge walked up to the stage, holding a sheaf of papers in his hand. He gave the marks and told each choir what was wrong with their singing and what was right. Joan's choir had the highest marks.

"We shall sing in the final concert and perhaps we shall be heard on the radio," Joan whispered to the girl beside her. "Now Bill will not be the only one."

Joan's big brother Bill was a member of the famous Kitsilano Boys' Band. They had toured Europe and the United States and won the world's championship. Sometimes Bill put on airs with his younger brothers and sisters.

The judge was in an excellent humor. He said it was ten years since he had first come from England for the annual contest at the Vancouver Musical Festival, and that the school choirs had been improving steadily ever since. He said so many kind things about their singing that they all felt proud and happy.

When Joan's choir lined up to take the street car back to their school, Joan asked leave to go with her mother to hear her cousin play in the piano contest in the Orange Hall.

There were twenty-two children in her cousin's class. Each in turn played the same piece. The stage was so large and empty and the grand piano so grand, that the pianists looked very small indeed. Joan grew tired of hearing the same piece over and over and wanted to tip-toe out. But she knew Aunt Irene would be offended if they did not wait to hear cousin Thelma play.

At last the piano contest was over and Joan jumped up, thinking hard about ice cream and cake to celebrate her choir's success. Her mother gave her an understanding smile, and they went out into the lovely spring afternoon.

"I was so excited, I could not eat my lunch," Joan said, as they looked about for the nearest ice cream parlor.

While they were eating their ice cream and cake, a girl of Joan's age came in with her mother and went to another table. Both mother and daughter had dark hair and dark, mournful eyes. The girl smiled at Joan and Joan smiled back.

"Who is that girl with the sweet smile and the sad eyes?" Joan's mother asked.

"Her name is Paula, and she is a refugee from Poland," Joan replied. "She is in my class at school. She can read English and do her lessons, but when she talks she uses her words differently. I often help her with her English."

"I see she has a violin case. She must be playing in the Festival," said Joan's mother.

"I'm so excited to think we'll be singing in the final concert on Saturday evening," Joan exclaimed, forgetting Paula. "Bill will no longer be the only musical person in the family."

Her mother laughed as she put on her gloves and stood up.

"I hope you aren't going to put on airs, too," she said. "I could not stand two conceited children in one family."

On Saturday evening Joan had a new white dress for the final concert, at which the winners in each class performed. Beyond the green plush curtains she could see rows and rows of faces, growing dim

in the far-back seats. Everyone was thrilled, for this was the peak of the Festival.

Joan was happy because she was one of the winning choir. Everything was gay. Everyone was well dressed and cheerful. It seemed as if all must be happy. Then a small, slight figure came on the stage and stood nestling a violin under her chin.

"Paula!" Joan whispered. "I didn't know she had won."

The strings quivered under Paula's bow. A cry of deep sorrow came from the violin, a song of wild longing, a tale of a homeland under a tyrant's rule. When the last note had died way, there was a moment's silence before the great audience started to clap.

Joan clasped her hands. "If only I could play the violin! It's wonderful to be able to play like that." All through the rest of the evening, Joan seemed to hear the cry of Paula's violin.

The whole Festival program went on the national radio network. The judge repeated his words of praise and the audience went wild. But through all the excitement Joan was thinking, "Paula can play the violin so that tears come in people's eyes. If only I could do that."

On Monday morning Joan spent all recess time and part of the noon hour helping Paula with her English. Paula was glowing with happiness over her success in the Festival. Sitting on Paula's desk, Joan asked questions about violins and learning to play them. She found that Paula had been studying violin since she was five.

After school Joan went home and emptied her china pig. Only twenty-three cents came out. She collected her doll buggy, roller skates, and the old watch Grandma had given her. The watch was a key-winder without a key, but it had a gold hunting case. She took them to an antique shop where she had seen a violin in the window.

The man in the antique shop took little interest in her collection until he saw the watch. "Not much good," he said. "Key-winder . . . no key. The mainspring is gone. I'll allow you a dollar for it."

Joan glanced up quickly. "It's real gold," she told him. "I think I'll take it to a jeweler and ask him what it's worth."

"Oh, I thought it was only gold plated," he exclaimed. "Real gold . . . that is different."

In the end Joan went out of the shop with the violin in a case, a bow that had been re-haired, a piece of resin, and a book of instructions. She was happier even than she had been when her school won the competition.

At home she shut herself in the room she shared with her sister Sally. She knew her father could not afford to let her take music lessons. Bill was going to a teacher, and Sally was learning the piano. She made up her mind to teach herself.

Mother was at a Red Cross meeting, Bill was at ball practice, and the children were at the park playground. The house was her own. Joan took the violin and bow out of the case and drew the bow across the strings. The result was an anguished wail. Outside, a neighbor's dog howled as if in answer.

"Pretty bad," she said to herself with a shudder. "I'd better read the book of instructions."

She laid the violin carefully on her bed and opened the book. At school she had learned to read

music, and that part was easy for her. But learning how to place her fingers on the strings, and how to hold the bow and draw it, would take months of practice.

"I'll keep it a secret until I can play a tune . . . or perhaps a scale," she decided, "so they won't laugh at me."

Hearing the front door open, she hastily put the violin and bow back in the case and hid them under the bed. She waited eagerly for another chance to practice and schemed to keep her secret from the family.

"I'll mop our room this week, Sally," Joan offered kindly, the following morning. "I know it's your turn, but you have your practicing to do." It made her feel uncomfortable to see the look of surprise in her mother's eyes as she took the mop and went upstairs.

It was fairly easy to keep the violin a secret while it was under the bed. The trouble was to find time to practice when no one was at home. The next evening Mother offered to take the whole family to the pictures.

"I'd rather stay home, Mother," Joan said. "I have some work to do."

Her mother looked puzzled, but did not ask any questions. As soon as the family had gone down the street, Joan bounded up the stairs and pulled the violin case from under the bed.

Having a good ear for music, she soon learned to tune the instrument. She rubbed the bow over the resin and then tried to play a scale. She had been wrestling with the scale for nearly a quarter of an hour, when she heard a sharp rap at the back door.

"Someone wanting to borrow a cup of sugar, I suppose," she thought, putting down the violin. She ran downstairs and found the next door neighbor at the door.

"Joan, are you all right?" the woman asked anxiously. "I saw your mother and the other children go away, and I heard such a queer noise! I was afraid something had happened to you."

Joan blushed crimson. She was afraid the neighbor would tell her mother about the noises, so she decided to take Mrs. Blake into her confidence.

"It's a violin," she whispered, "and I'm keeping it a secret until I can play a scale."

Mrs. Blake frowned. "We have lived through Bill's cornet and Sally's piano, but I guess your violin will send us looking for another house." She stalked off with an annoyed twitch of her shoulders.

Sally was the next person to find out about the violin. She was hunting for her running shoes and started poking under Joan's bed.

"Whatever have you got under here, Joan?"

Now the secret was out and everyone in the house groaned as if it were bad news. After that there was no use waiting for the family to go out, and Joan practiced whenever she had time.

"Look, Joan, do you have to practice before breakfast?" Sally asked. "There's a man who plays on a saw. Why not buy a second-hand saw instead of a violin?"

Joan flushed and bit her lip. She knew she must not lose her temper if she hoped to be allowed to go on with her practicing.

"See here, Joan," Bill told her firmly, "I hate to spoil your fun, but that fiddle is driving me crazy. As soon as I have a job playing in a dance orchestra, I'll buy you a good one and pay for lessons—that is, I will, if you will sell this one."

The tears filled Joan's eyes like sea water coming

into a hole in the beach. "By that time I'll be too
old to learn."

"As a matter of fact," Bill sawed the air with his
hand, "you are too old now. Five is the age to start."

As they walked down the school steps at recess
next day, Paula asked Joan why she looked so un-
happy.

"I have to sell my violin," Joan confessed, "because I make such gruesome sounds on it. Bill can't
stand it."

46

Paula raised her eyebrows in a funny little quirk. "Is your teacher then not so good?"

"I can't afford a teacher."

Paula looked puzzled, then thoughtful, and at last pleased.

"What do you say, my dear friend? You have taught me the English, will you permit that I teach you the violin, yes?"

Joan's face grew brighter, but she still hesitated. "I have no money to pay you, Paula."

The Polish girl laughed and put her arm round Joan's waist. "We shall trade lessons in English for lessons in violin. That I shall so much like."

Joan smiled. "That will be wonderful, Paula. Let's keep it a secret till I can play a piece, shall we?"

For a month Joan's family wondered why she was looking like the cat that ate the canary. Then one evening she brought down her violin and played Brahms' "Lullaby."

"Now, must I sell my violin?" she demanded.

Big brother Bill grinned. "You'll do, Joan. You'll be a violinist yet, if you keep on."

YOUNG FIRE WARDEN

Greta admired her big brother Stan in his new uniform almost as much as he admired himself. She was three years younger than Stan, who was thirteen. He wore a red shirt with an evergreen tree on the pocket and a green cap, shaped like an airman's. It was the uniform of a Junior Fire Warden.

48

Stan and Greta lived in a scow house belonging to the Princess Inlet Logging Company, on the coast of British Columbia. The loggers' scow houses could easily be towed to a fresh place when one stand of timber was logged off. Stan and Greta went to school at a fishing village four miles away, traveling to and fro in a small boat with an outboard motor.

Stan looked at himself in the mirror and cocked his cap on the side of his head. A fair-haired, freckle-faced boy with blue eyes grinned back at him from the mirror. Stan was like a young tree, slim and straight and strong.

Greta was a copy of Stan, except that she was smaller. She was dressed in a blue shirt and slacks and wore a blue ribbon around her brown curls.

"If you have finished admiring yourself, let's go and pick blueberries," Greta suggested.

That was one thing Stan was always willing to do, for he did love blueberry pie, especially those Mother made. During vacation there was plenty of time for fishing and picking wild fruit. The Indians made jam of the purple salal berries, but the wild taste did not appeal to Stan and Greta.

They liked to pick the small blackberries, whose long creeping vines spread over the earth and rocks, and the small red huckleberries and the large blueberries. They left the salal, the mountain ash, and the elderberries to those who liked them.

Stan and Greta set off, each carrying an Indian basket woven of root fibers in a pattern of two colors. They climbed an old skid-road to logged-off land on which the blueberries, huckleberries, blackberries, and fireweed had grown up in a tangle.

It was blistery hot on the hillside, and after a while Greta began to tire.

"Let's rest in the shade of a tree," she begged.

Stan looked around him. "All right, if we can find a tree out in the slash," he said. "You know there's a new order that no one may go into the bush until we have rain. This long dry spell has made it too dangerous for fires. That's why most of the loggers went to town today. Camp is closed down for the present."

Greta sighed and said, "Then I'll just have to stand this heat a little longer."

They went on picking until their baskets were full. Then Greta lay down in the shade of a huckleberry bush. Stan sat beside her and began eating blueberries out of his basket.

"How would you like to go up and see the young Douglas firs the Forestry men planted last March?" he asked.

"When I've had a little more rest," Greta agreed,

"I'd like to see the Douglas firs. Do you know why they planted them? You would think, with such a lot of cones falling, they would plant themselves."

"Cones fall, but they don't blow about like fire-weed onto logged-off areas," Stan explained, "and we're cutting the forests so fast that we have to plant young trees, or there will be no timber."

Greta lay and looked up at the sky. It was so deeply blue that she could go on looking at it for an hour without getting tired. A very white cloud drifted over, the shape of a camel with a man on its back.

Stan was gazing out to sea. He could recognize every craft in sight. A few fishing boats were passing, a passenger steamer with a red-and-black funnel, and a tug with a boom of logs. Far out an extra strong tug towed a cigar-shaped boom of Sitka spruce logs from the Queen Charlotte Islands.

"When a baby spruce is growing up, it doesn't know whether it will be an airplane or a newspaper or hundreds of pairs of stockings," he remarked, pointing out the boom to Greta. "Those spruce logs are going to the pulp mills at Powell River to be turned into newsprint."

Greta knew that Stan took a keen interest in trees and the logging work. He liked to watch the high rigger fastening guy ropes and steel cables to a tall standing tree, so that the men could pull the cut logs out of the bush after the big saws had cut them.

52

He liked to hear the cry of "Timber!"—the warning that a tree was about to fall—and to listen to the busy puffing of the donkey engine at the base of the "spar" tree. This engine did the work of hauling the huge logs and piling them in the "cold decks," waiting for spring.

Sometimes the logs are hauled to the sea by a caterpillar tractor, which the loggers call a "cat." When there is a stream at hand they build a flume, or trough, to carry the logs to the sea—the "salt chuck." There they are gathered in booms and towed to the sawmill by strong tugs.

Stan knew all the different kinds of trees and what they are used for. He loved the tall, stately Douglas firs, which in the days of sailing ships were used for masts. They are splendid for anything that requires straight strong timbers, like flag poles, flooring, or plywood.

Stan pointed to a bluish tree at the edge of the clearing. "Do you know what that is, Greta?"

"No, I don't," Greta replied patiently. She knew the question was just Stan's way of showing her that he did know.

"It's a Sitka spruce. They're the best wood for airplane parts, but not many grow here. Over on the Queen Charlotte Islands there are lots of them."

"I know a hemlock when I see it by the way its tip flops over," Greta said, to prove that she was not entirely ignorant. "And I know a cedar and that it grows near water and makes good shingles. Right now, I wish it wasn't so hot."

"It will soon be cooler," Stan predicted. "The sky is clouding over. Let's go on up and see that Douglas fir plantation."

"I don't want to carry this heavy basket up the hill. Let's leave the baskets here and cover them with leaves till we come back," Greta suggested.

Stan agreed. They placed the baskets side by side, close to the bush, and covered them with huckleberry boughs. Then they climbed up the hill to the area that

the Government had planted with young firs the previous March.

Stan looked at the sky. "It's going to rain," he observed.

"Let it," Greta replied. "It's so hot I'd love it."

Clouds were rolling over the mountain, silvery white at the edges but dark and threatening below. As they watched, a cloud split open in a jagged crack of light. Immediately afterward came a sharp report, like a pistol shot, followed by a roll of thunder.

"The storm must be close," said Stan. "The thunder came so soon after the lightning. There it goes again!" He took off his Fire Warden's cap and tucked it into the top of his trousers, under his belt. "I'd hate to have my new uniform soaked. Let's take a short cut home."

"But our berries!" Greta protested. "We don't want to lose them after all the work of picking them. It's not much farther that way."

Stan didn't want to say good-by to those blueberry pies either, so he ran with Greta. Often they were caught in tangles of blackberry bramble or tripped by branches on the ground.

The lightning flashes were coming with scarcely a breath between, and the rolling of the thunder was almost continuous. But in spite of all this noise and fury, hardly any rain fell. A small scurry of light drops swept over them, but that was all.

As they reached the place where they had left the berries, Greta gave an anguished wail.

"Look, Stan! A bear is eating our berries!"

"It was your idea to leave them there."

A black bear had tipped over one basket and the berries were fast disappearing. Stan and Greta looked at each other.

"What shall we do?" asked Greta.

"Drive him off," was Stan's advice.

"He might turn nasty if we interrupt his meal."

Just then the bear raised his head, and seeing two human beings, ambled away as if he felt a prick of conscience. When he was at a safe distance Stan and Greta salvaged the remainder of the berries.

They were starting home, when a sharper crack than any before startled them. A tall fir tree on the hillside flared up like a monster match. There was another crack and another tree went up in flames. With no rain to put out the blaze, trees close by caught fire from those that were struck.

"Take my basket," Stan ordered. "I'll have to run for all I'm worth to report the fire. It's in the Company's stand of timber."

By now the storm was traveling farther away, striking trees here and there. Not a drop of water

fell and this dry thunderstorm was even worse than a careless camper.

It is a terrible thing when the great forests are set on fire. Not only millions of feet of lumber are destroyed, but the rabbits, bears, marmots, squirrels, deer, porcupines, and birds die in agony. Stan knew this, and to report this fire was his first official task since putting on his junior Fire Warden's uniform.

The tide was down, and the sections of the landing-stage that led to the scow colony lay sprawled and uneven on the shingle. Stan ran down them, sure-footed as a Rocky Mountain goat, and burst into the office. His father was there, talking to the Government log-scaler, who measures the stumpage to make sure the logging company is paying the correct amount of tax to the Government.

"The lightning started a fire in the green timber, Dad," Stan gasped.

"In the green timber!" His father jumped up. "And here I am with only a few men in camp. Never mind—we'll get going right away. We have a million feet of cold deck up there . . . we'll have to save it."

In a few minutes the loggers were on their way up the hill, guided by Stan and the plume of smoke that was already billowing up, white and yellow,

from the green timber. They carried axes, picks and shovels, and a pail.

Stan led the men by the shortest route to the fire. They met Greta on her way down. She passed them with a smile and a wave of the hand.

Fighting fire on the side of a mountain is a hard and dangerous job, even for husky loggers.

"You've done your part, Stan; now keep out of the way," his father ordered. "I'll take your shovel."

Soon trees were toppling, their crests crashing to the ground, where the loggers threw earth on the flames and beat them out with shovels. Sometimes a tree pitched headlong down a gulley, bringing a small avalanche of rocks and earth behind it.

Stan stayed in the clearing, watching. Soon he thought of something useful to do. He carried the pail to the creek and filled it with water for the fire-fighters to drink. One after another they came and drank in great gulps.

"You're doing more good this way than you could with a shovel," his father said, drawing his hand across his mouth and leaving a black mustache.

Stan felt like laughing at his father's black face until he noticed that black flakes were settling on his own new red shirt. The grin wiped itself off his face very suddenly. He peeled off the shirt, shook it well, folded it and hid it under a bush.

Then he set off to the creek for more water. When he came back he noticed that there was much less smoke, and the flames were almost quenched. The men were digging around the burned area and heaping earth on the charred logs in which embers still glowed. After a while Stan's father came to him, a happy smile on his face.

"I guess we can call it a day. One man can watch it now. You've saved the Company a lot of money, son. With the wind the way it is, the fire would soon have been in the cold-deck logs."

Stan went for his red shirt and pulled it on. He was proud of the few black smudges now. They proved he had a real right to wear the uniform of a Junior Fire Warden.

GLOSSARY

boom—a sort of fence of logs in the water, joined by chains, in which loose logs are kept. These booms may be fastened together in different ways for towing.

bush—the forest.

cold deck—logs freshly cut which are piled up and left until spring when they can be hauled or floated to the sea.

dinghy—a small rowboat for going ashore from an anchored yacht or gas-boat.

drift—the fisherman lets out the gill-net and allows his boat to drift for some hours before hauling in the net. This period is called a "drift."

fireweed—a tall weed with magenta flowers that grows on land ravaged by forest fires.

flume—a wooden trough, sometimes miles long, into which a stream of water can be turned, to float logs to the sea.

freeboard—the part of the boat's hull above water.

gill-net—a net for catching salmon by the gills.

guy ropes—ropes to hold the spar tree steady against the strain.

high rigger—a logger who climbs very high trees to cut off the tops so that they may be used as "spar trees," to which cables are attached for hauling felled trees to the "cold decks," or piles of logs freshly cut.

humpies—hump-backed salmon, a species not so good as sockeye.

log-scaler—an official who measures logs.

marmots—small animals like coneys.

Powell River—a town in northern British Columbia, noted for pulp mills.

Queen Charlotte Islands—near the coast of British Columbia, northwest of Vancouver Island.

salal—an evergreen bush with purple berries used by Indians to make jam.

salt chuck—lumbermen's term for salt water, the sea.

scow—like a barge, large and flat-bottomed, and without means of locomotion.

shingle—beach covered with small pebbles and stones.

Sitka—a region in Alaska named after the Sitka Indians. The name also applies to a species of spruce which attains a great size.

slash—a cut-over area where the branches, tops and so forth (slashings) lie on the ground.

sockeye—probably from appearance of eye. Best for canning because of bright red color and large oil content.

spar tree—a tall topped tree to which cables are attached for hauling out logs.

stand of timber—area of land covered with trees suitable for logging.

stumpage—a charge based on stumps left by logging operations.

Acknowledgment is gratefully made to the British Columbia Travel Bureau for photographs used by the artist.